6	7	8	9	10	11	12
13	14	15	16	17	18	19
20	21	22	23	24	25	26
27	28	29	30			

4	5	6	7	8	9	10
11	12	13	14	15	16	17
18	19	20	21	22	23	24
25	26	27	28	29	30	31

BrownTrout Publishers, Inc.

Connecting People to Their Passions

browntrout.com

facebook.com/browntroutpublishers

pinterest.com/browntroutpub

@browntroutpub

USA—World Headquarters
201 Continental Blvd., Suite 200
El Segundo, CA 90245 USA
310 607 9010 | Toll Free 800 777 7812
sales@browntrout.com

Canada Toll Free 1 888 254 5842 | sales@browntrout.ca
Australia and New Zealand enquiries@browntrout.com.au
Australia Toll Free 1 800 111 882
New Zealand Toll Free 0 800 888 112

Times are in Universal Time (UT) which, adjusted to the reader's time
dates of lunar events. Publisher is not responsible or liable for any rel
event dates. No portion of this calendar may be reproduced, digitized,
without prior written permission from the publisher.

BrownTrout honors its commitment to sustainability by choosing F
vegetable-based inks, a digital workflow, and the practice of recyc

The components of this calendar are recyclable depending on the
Please check with your local recycler.

janvier | enero

SUNDAY dim | dom	MONDAY lun | lun	TUESDAY mar | mar	WEDNESDAY mer | miér	THURSDAY jeu | jue	FRIDAY ven | vier	SATURDAY sam | sáb
1 New Year's Day	2 New Year's Day observed (AU; NZ; UK)	3 Day after New Year's Day observed (NZ; SCT)	4	5	6 Full Moon 23:08 UT ○ Epiphany Día de los Reyes (MX)	7
8	9	10	11	12	13	14
15 Last Quarter 2:10 UT ◑	16 Martin Luther King Jr. Day (US)	17	18	19	20	21 New Moon 20:53 UT ● Klara Birthday
22 Chinese New Year (Rabbit)	23	24	25 Burns Night (SCT)	26 Australia Day (AU)	27 Int'l Holocaust Remembrance Day (UN)	28 First Quarter 15:19 UT ◐
29	30	31	1	2		

DECEMBER 2022

S	M	T	W	T	F	S
				1	2	3
4	5	6	7	8	9	10
11	12	13	14	15	16	17
18	19	20	21	22	23	24
25	26	27	28	29	30	31

FEBRUARY 2023

S	M	T	W	T	F	S
			1	2	3	4
5	6	7	8	9	10	11
12	13	14	15	16	17	18
19	20	21	22	23	24	25
26	27	28				

2023

FEBRUARY

février | febrero

SUNDAY dim | dom	MONDAY lun | lun	TUESDAY mar | mar	WEDNESDAY mer | miér	THURSDAY jeu | jue	FRIDAY ven | vier	SATURDAY sam | sáb
29	30	31	1	2 Groundhog Day (US; CAN) Día de la Candelaria (MX)	3	4
5 Full Moon 18:28 UT ○ Día de la Constitución (MX)	6 Waitangi Day (NZ)	7	8	9	10	11
12 Lincoln's Birthday (US)	13 Last Quarter 16:01 UT ◑	14 Valentine's Day	15	16	17	18
19	20 New Moon 7:06 UT ● Presidents' Day (US) Provincial Holiday (CAN except NL/QC)	21 Shrove Tuesday Mardi Gras	22 Ash Wednesday Washington's Birthday (US)	23	24 Día de la Bandera (MX)	25
26	27 First Quarter 8:05 UT ◐ Great Lent begins (Orthodox)	28	1	2		

JANUARY 2023

S	M	T	W	T	F	S
1	2	3	4	5	6	7
8	9	10	11	12	13	14
15	16	17	18	19	20	21
22	23	24	25	26	27	28
29	30	31				

MARCH 2023

S	M	T	W	T	F	S
			1	2	3	4
5	6	7	8	9	10	11
12	13	14	15	16	17	18
19	20	21	22	23	24	25
26	27	28	29	30	31	

mars | marzo

SUNDAY dim | dom	MONDAY lun | lun	TUESDAY mar | mar	WEDNESDAY mer | miér	THURSDAY jeu | jue	FRIDAY ven | vier	SATURDAY sam | sáb
FEBRUARY 2023 S M T W T F S 1 2 3 4 5 6 7 8 9 10 11 12 13 14 15 16 17 18 19 20 21 22 23 24 25 26 27 28	**APRIL** 2023 S M T W T F S 1 2 3 4 5 6 7 8 9 10 11 12 13 14 15 16 17 18 19 20 21 22 23 24 25 26 27 28 29 30	28	1 Autumn begins (S. Hemisphere) St. David's Day (WAL)	2	3	4
5	6 Labour Day (WA-AU) Purim begins at sundown	7 Full Moon 12:40 UT ○	8 Int'l Women's Day	9	10	11
12 Daylight Saving Time begins (US; CAN)	13 Commonwealth Day (UK) Canberra Day (ACT-AU) Eight Hours Day (TAS-AU) Labour Day (VIC-AU)	14	15 Last Quarter 2:08 UT ◑	16	17 St. Patrick's Day	18
19 Mothering Sunday (UK)	20 Spring begins (N. Hemisphere)	21 New Moon 17:23 UT ●	22 Ramadan begins at sundown	23	24	25
26	27	28	29 First Quarter 2:32 UT ◐	30	31	1

avril | abril

SUNDAY dim | dom	MONDAY lun | lun	TUESDAY mar | mar	WEDNESDAY mer | miér	THURSDAY jeu | jue	FRIDAY ven | vier	SATURDAY sam | sáb
MARCH 2023 S M T W T F S 1 2 3 4 5 6 7 8 9 10 11 12 13 14 15 16 17 18 19 20 21 22 23 24 25 26 27 28 29 30 31	**MAY** 2023 S M T W T F S 1 2 3 4 5 6 7 8 9 10 11 12 13 14 15 16 17 18 19 20 21 22 23 24 25 26 27 28 29 30 31	28	29	30	31	1 April Fools' Day
2 Palm Sunday Daylight Saving Time ends (AU except NT/QLD/WA; NZ)	3	4	5 Passover begins at sundown	Full Moon 4:34 UT ○ 6 Maundy Thursday	7 Good Friday Bank Holiday (UK)	8 Holy Saturday
9 Easter Sunday	10 Easter Monday Bank Holiday (UK except SCT; IRL)	11	12	Last Quarter 9:11 UT ◑ 13	14	15
16 Pascha (Orthodox)	17 Yom HaShoah begins at sundown	18	19	New Moon 4:12 UT ● 20	21 Birthday of Queen Elizabeth II (AU; CAN; NZ; UK) Eid al-Fitr begins at sundown	22 Earth Day
St. George's Day (ENG; NL-CAN) 23 30 Día del Niño (MX)	24	25 Anzac Day (AU; NZ)	26 Administrative Professionals Day	First Quarter 21:20 UT ◐ 27 Koningsdag (NL)	28 Arbor Day (US)	29

mai | mayo

SUNDAY dim | dom	MONDAY lun | lun	TUESDAY mar | mar	WEDNESDAY mer | miér	THURSDAY jeu | jue	FRIDAY ven | vier	SATURDAY sam | sáb
30	1 May Day | Int'l Workers' Day Bank/Public Holiday (UK; IRL) Día del Trabajo (MX) Labour Day (QLD-AU) Dag van de Arbeid (BE; NL)	2	3	4 National Day of Prayer (US) Dodenherdenking (NL)	Full Moon 17:34 UT ○ 5 Cinco de Mayo (US) Batalla de Puebla (MX) Bevrijdingsdag (NL)	6
7 National Pet Week (US)	8 Fête de la Victoire (FR)	9	10 Día de las Madres (MX)	11	Last Quarter 14:28 UT ◑ 12	13
14 Mother's Day (US; AU; BE; CAN; NL; NZ)	15 Día del Maestro (MX)	16	17	18 Ascension	New Moon 15:53 UT ● 19	20 Armed Forces Day (US)
21	22 Victoria Day/ Fête de la Reine (CAN) Journée nationale des patriotes/ National Patriots' Day (QC-CAN)	23	24	25	26 National Sorry Day (AU)	First Quarter 15:22 UT ◐ 27
28 Pentecost (Whitsun)	29 Pentecost Monday Memorial Day (US) Spring Bank Holiday (UK) Reconciliation Day (ACT-AU)	30	31	1		

APRIL 2023

S	M	T	W	T	F	S
						1
2	3	4	5	6	7	8
9	10	11	12	13	14	15
16	17	18	19	20	21	22
23	24	25	26	27	28	29
30						

JUNE 2023

S	M	T	W	T	F	S
				1	2	3
4	5	6	7	8	9	10
11	12	13	14	15	16	17
18	19	20	21	22	23	24
25	26	27	28	29	30	

2023 JUNE

juin | junio

SUNDAY dim | dom	MONDAY lun | lun	TUESDAY mar | mar	WEDNESDAY mer | miér	THURSDAY jeu | jue	FRIDAY ven | vier	SATURDAY sam | sáb
MAY 2023 S M T W T F S 1 2 3 4 5 6 7 8 9 10 11 12 13 14 15 16 17 18 19 20 21 22 23 24 25 26 27 28 29 30 31	**JULY** 2023 S M T W T F S 1 2 3 4 5 6 7 8 9 10 11 12 13 14 15 16 17 18 19 20 21 22 23 24 25 26 27 28 29 30 31	30	31	1 Winter begins (S. Hemisphere)	2	3
Full Moon 3:42 UT ○ 4 Fête des Mères (FR)	5 Public Holiday (IRL) Queen's Birthday (NZ) Western Australia Day (WA-AU)	6	7	8	9	Last Quarter 19:31 UT ◑ 10 Queen's Official Birthday (tentative) (UK)
11 Vaderdag/Fête des Pères (BE)	12 Queen's Birthday (AU except QLD/WA)	13	14 Flag Day (US)	15	16	17
New Moon 4:37 UT ● 18 Father's Day (US; CAN; FR; MX; NL; UK)	19 Juneteenth (US)	20	21 Summer begins (N. Hemisphere) National Indigenous Peoples Day (NT/YT-CAN)	22	23	24 Fête nationale du Québec/ National Holiday of Quebec (QC-CAN)
25	First Quarter 7:50 UT ◐ 26 June Holiday (NL-CAN)	27	28 Eid al-Adha begins at sundown	29	30	1

juillet | julio

SUNDAY dim | dom	MONDAY lun | lun	TUESDAY mar | mar	WEDNESDAY mer | miér	THURSDAY jeu | jue	FRIDAY ven | vier	SATURDAY sam | sáb
JUNE 2023 S M T W T F S 1 2 3 4 5 6 7 8 9 10 11 12 13 14 15 16 17 18 19 20 21 22 23 24 25 26 27 28 29 30	**AUGUST** 2023 S M T W T F S 1 2 3 4 5 6 7 8 9 10 11 12 13 14 15 16 17 18 19 20 21 22 23 24 25 26 27 28 29 30 31	27	28	29	30	1 Canada Day/Fête du Canada (CAN)
2	3 Full Moon 11:39 UT ○	4 Independence Day (US)	5	6	7	8
9 Nunavut Day (NU-CAN)	10 Last Quarter 1:48 UT ◑	11 Feest van de Vlaamse Gemeenschap (BE)	12 Bank Holiday (NIR)	13	14 Fête nationale de la France (FR)	15
16	17 New Moon 18:32 UT ●	18 Muharram begins at sundown	19	20	21 Nationale feestdag/ Fête nationale de la Belgique (BE)	22
23 / 30	24 / 31	25 First Quarter 22:07 UT ◐	26	27 Ashura begins at sundown	28	29

août | agosto

SUNDAY dim | dom	MONDAY lun | lun	TUESDAY mar | mar	WEDNESDAY mer | miér	THURSDAY jeu | jue	FRIDAY ven | vier	SATURDAY sam | sáb
JULY 2023 S M T W T F S 1 2 3 4 5 6 7 8 9 10 11 12 13 14 15 16 17 18 19 20 21 22 23 24 25 26 27 28 29 30 31	**SEPTEMBER** 2023 S M T W T F S 1 2 3 4 5 6 7 8 9 10 11 12 13 14 15 16 17 18 19 20 21 22 23 24 25 26 27 28 29 30	1 Full Moon 18:32 UT ○	2	3	4	5
6	7 Civic Holiday/Congé civique (CAN except NL/QC/YT) Bank Holiday (IRL; SCT) Picnic Day (NT-AU)	8 Last Quarter 10:28 UT ◑	9	10	11	12 My B-Day
13	14	15 Assumption	16 New Moon 9:38 UT ● Royal Queensland Show (QLD-AU)	17	18	19
20	21 Discovery Day (YT-CAN)	22	23	24 First Quarter 9:57 UT ◐	25	26
27	28 Summer Bank Holiday (UK except SCT)	29	30	31 Full Moon 1:35 UT ○	1	2

2023

SEPTEMBER

septembre | septiembre

SUNDAY dim | dom	MONDAY lun | lun	TUESDAY mar | mar	WEDNESDAY mer | miér	THURSDAY jeu | jue	FRIDAY ven | vier	SATURDAY sam | sáb
AUGUST 2023 S M T W T F S 1 2 3 4 5 6 7 8 9 10 11 12 13 14 15 16 17 18 19 20 21 22 23 24 25 26 27 28 29 30 31	**OCTOBER** 2023 S M T W T F S 1 2 3 4 5 6 7 8 9 10 11 12 13 14 15 16 17 18 19 20 21 22 23 24 25 26 27 28 29 30 31	29	30	31	1 Spring begins (S. Hemisphere)	2
3 Father's Day (AU; NZ)	4 Labor Day (US) Labour Day/Fête du travail (CAN)	5	6 Last Quarter 22:21 UT ◑	7	8	9
10 National Grandparents Day (US)	11 Patriot Day/National Day of Service and Remembrance (US)	12	13	14	15 New Moon 1:40 UT ● Noche del Grito (MX) Rosh Hashanah begins at sundown	16 Día de la Independencia (MX)
17 Australian Citizenship Day (AU)	18	19	20	21 UN Int'l Day of Peace	22 First Quarter 19:32 UT ◐	23 Autumn begins (N. Hemisphere)
24 Daylight Saving Time begins (NZ) Yom Kippur begins at sundown	25 Queen's Birthday (WA-AU)	26	27 Fête de la Communauté Française (BE)	28	29 Full Moon 9:57 UT ○	30

2023

OCTOBER

octobre | octubre

SUNDAY dim | dom	MONDAY lun | lun	TUESDAY mar | mar	WEDNESDAY mer | miér	THURSDAY jeu | jue	FRIDAY ven | vier	SATURDAY sam | sáb
1 Daylight Saving Time begins (AU except NT/QLD/WA)	2 Labour Day (ACT/NSW/SA-AU) Queen's Birthday (QLD-AU)	3	4 World Animal Day	5	6 Last Quarter 13:48 UT ◑	7
8	9 Indigenous Peoples' Day/ Columbus Day (US) Thanksgiving Day/ Action de grâce (CAN)	10	11	12 Día de la Raza (MX)	13	14 New Moon 17:55 UT ●
15	16 Boss's Day	17	18	19	20	21
22 First Quarter 3:29 UT ◐	23 Labour Day (NZ)	24 United Nations Day	25	26	27	28 Full Moon 20:24 UT ○
29	30 Public Holiday (IRL)	31 Halloween	1	2		

SEPTEMBER 2023

S	M	T	W	T	F	S
					1	2
3	4	5	6	7	8	9
10	11	12	13	14	15	16
17	18	19	20	21	22	23
24	25	26	27	28	29	30

NOVEMBER 2023

S	M	T	W	T	F	S
			1	2	3	4
5	6	7	8	9	10	11
12	13	14	15	16	17	18
19	20	21	22	23	24	25
26	27	28	29	30		

2023

NOVEMBER

novembre | noviembre

SUNDAY dim | dom	MONDAY lun | lun	TUESDAY mar | mar	WEDNESDAY mer | miér	THURSDAY jeu | jue	FRIDAY ven | vier	SATURDAY sam | sáb
OCTOBER 2023 (see below)	DECEMBER 2023 (see below)	31	1 All Saints' Day	2 All Souls' Day; Día de los Muertos (MX)	3	4
5 Last Quarter 8:37 UT ◑ Guy Fawkes Night (NZ; UK) Daylight Saving Time ends (US; CAN)	6	7 Election Day (US) Melbourne Cup (VIC-AU)	8	9	10 Veterans Day observed (US)	11 Veterans Day (US) Remembrance Day (AU; CAN; NZ) Armistice (BE; FR)
12 Remembrance Sunday (UK)	13 New Moon 9:27 UT ●	14	15 Koningsdag/Fête du Roi (BE)	16	17	18
19	20 First Quarter 10:50 UT ◐ Día de la Revolución Mexicana (MX)	21	22	23 Thanksgiving Day (US)	24	25
26	27 Full Moon 9:16 UT ○	28	29	30 St. Andrew's Day (SCT)	1	2

OCTOBER 2023

S	M	T	W	T	F	S
1	2	3	4	5	6	7
8	9	10	11	12	13	14
15	16	17	18	19	20	21
22	23	24	25	26	27	28
29	30	31				

DECEMBER 2023

S	M	T	W	T	F	S
					1	2
3	4	5	6	7	8	9
10	11	12	13	14	15	16
17	18	19	20	21	22	23
24	25	26	27	28	29	30
31